D1529872

Never Stop Exploring!

Tracie Harang

Brady Harang

 **Tango**

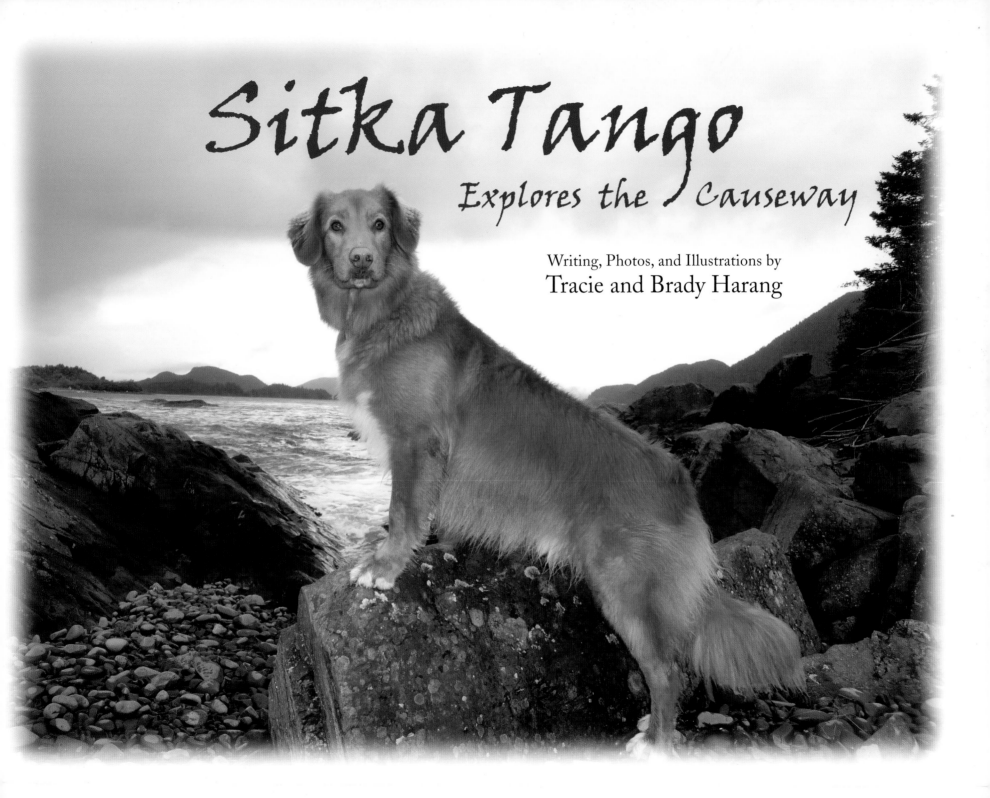

Sitka Tango
Explores the Causeway

Writing, Photos, and Illustrations by
Tracie and Brady Harang

Peanut Butter Publishing
2925 Fairview Avenue East
Seattle, Washington 98102
877-728-8837
www.peanutbutterpublishing.com

Dedication

To Brady's great grandparents; Ola and Marian Harang, Ron and Letty Unterwegner, and Warren and Anna Pellett, all of whom moved to the Sitka area in the 50s and 60s, working hard and leaving footprints.

Acknowledgements

We would like to thank the Mt. Edgecumbe business class and The Printing Cove
for their hard work to help us design the first edition of this book.

Shanel Kusma and Ariel Soplu, thank you for sharing your talents,
your hard work, and great attitudes with this project!

Thank you to SEACC (Southeast Alaska Career Center) and Karen Martinsen for your wonderful
programs aimed towards educating and encouraging our youth to learn various trades.

Also, thank you to Rhea Ehresmann for your time and efforts!

Matthew Hunter has created a great website www.sitkaww2.com,
which was a resource for this book.

A giant thank you to Justin Harang (Brady's big brother) for
allowing us to use a few of your Causeway pictures!

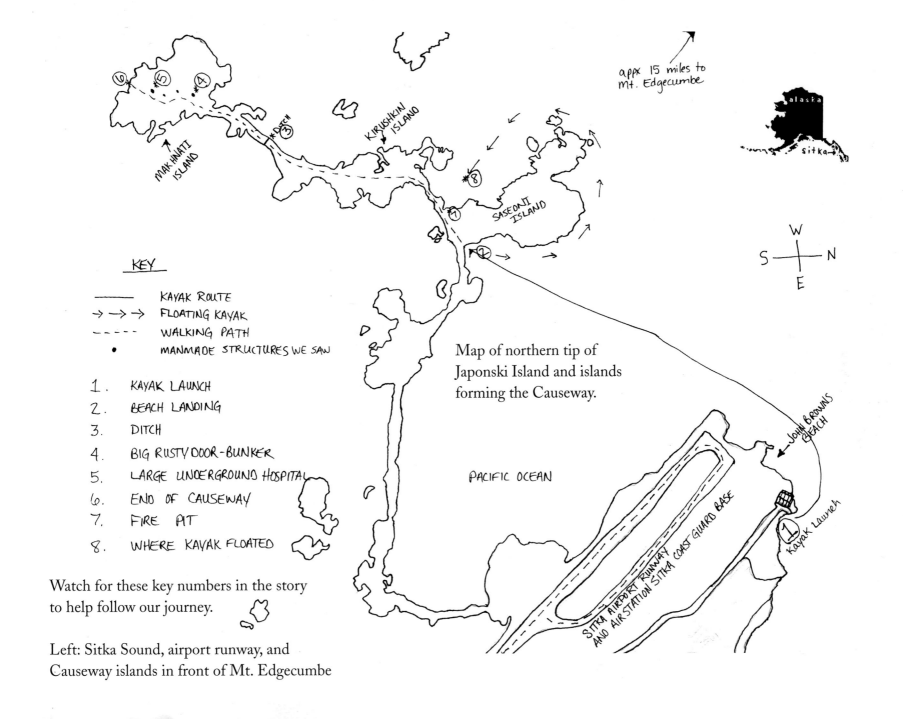

KEY

———— KAYAK ROUTE
→ → → FLOATING KAYAK
- - - - - WALKING PATH
• MANMADE STRUCTURES WE SAW

1. KAYAK LAUNCH
2. BEACH LANDING
3. DITCH
4. BIG RUSTY DOOR-BUNKER
5. LARGE UNDERGROUND HOSPITAL
6. END OF CAUSEWAY
7. FIRE PIT
8. WHERE KAYAK FLOATED

Watch for these key numbers in the story
to help follow our journey.

Left: Sitka Sound, airport runway, and
Causeway islands in front of Mt. Edgecumbe

Map of northern tip of
Japonski Island and islands
forming the Causeway.

PACIFIC OCEAN

appx 15 miles to
Mt. Edgecumbe

alaska
sitka

MAKHNATI ISLAND
KIRUSHKIN ISLAND
SASEDNI ISLAND
DITCH
JOHN BROWNS BEACH
SITKA AIRPORT RUNWAY
AND AIRSTATION SITKA COAST GUARD BASE
Kayak Launch

W
S — N
E

Sitka Tango loves adventure. He has a great life in Sitka, Alaska with a family that lives in a home overlooking the ocean and many islands surrounding Sitka. Tango especially loves to play with the three children in his family. Today, Brady, one of those children, is very eager to explore the Causeway and asked Tango to join him.

Brady, a 5th grader in Sitka, learned about the Causeway from school while studying World War II. The Causeway consists of eight islands connected by boulders to form a long, narrow point that is attached to the town of Sitka at the airport runway. The problem is, people cannot cross the runway, so the Causeway is only accessible by boat.

Looking through "Devil's Club" toward
Sitka from Makhnati Island.

3

Brady was excited to go to the Causeway because there were underground caves, bunkers, hospitals, and numerous gun batteries built into the islands over 60 years ago in the 1940s by soldiers preparing for the possibility of battle. This sounded very exciting to a young boy, and since Brady had a little kayak, he and Tango set off on a journey.

Tango did not need any gear, but Brady had to remember his chest waders, his fanny pack full of emergency items, and his life jacket! Brady and Tango started off by launching his kayak with his mom's help near John Brown's Beach. (1)* They paddled one mile from there, around the airport runway, and into a little cove, where Brady carefully tied up his kayak to a big rock on the beach. (2) *See map on page 1.

Brady and Tango soon learned that
the trail out to the caves and hospital
was washed out and rugged from the
huge waves that pound the Causeway
every day of the year. It was a very
difficult walk for Brady, but Tango
had no problems! Some of the huge
boulders were very steep to climb, but
the two explorers kept going.

Tango stayed by Brady the entire time as if guiding and protecting him. Brady was so proud of him! Along the way, they found numerous concrete structures that were now covered by moss and surrounded by trees. Brady had fun running on the top of the concrete and playing hide and go seek with Tango.

The trail snaked in and out of the thick forest. Even with the sun shining, parts of the forest were damp and dark...the perfect place to find interesting mushrooms!

Just over half way to the bunkers, Brady and Tango had a problem. The tide was extremely high that day, and water was covering the rocks! (3)

Brady had checked the tide book that morning and knew that there was going to be a bit of a wait for the tide to go back out. Even though Tango could easily swim across the ditch, he waited patiently next to Brady.

When they finally crossed the jagged boulders, it was still very deep, and Brady had to balance carefully while the surge of the water pulled at his legs!

Soon, they reached the first underground cave.
(4) A huge rusty door led the way into a large,
pitch-black room. Brady wished that he had
remembered a flashlight in his fanny pack! The
ceiling was around 15 feet high, and Brady could
not even see where the wall ended in the back.
It was spooky, and his voice echoed so loudly!

As Brady and Tango continued toward the end of the island, they passed up numerous large concrete structures that were camouflaged into the rocky hillside. Brady was amazed at the number of structures and how big some of them were. He tried to envision the challenges that the soldiers faced in 1942. With each passing year, the moss, trees, and brush had moved in on the structures. Brady was glad that they were made out of concrete!

Brady was excited to finally discover the underground hospital. (5) The wide hallway was lined on one side with rooms hidden behind creaky, old, wooden doors. As they slowly crept down the hall, it was becoming darker and darker. Brady was feeling his heart beat faster with each step. He was running his fingers along the damp wall to find his way in the dark. Suddenly, his foot landed on a loose metal hatch cover which banged like a snare drum against the concrete floor. Tango jumped, Brady squealed, and they both high-tailed it back out of the cave!

They finally reached the tip of the island where they sat and enjoyed the incredible view. (6) The sun had popped out and the volcano named Mt. Edgecumbe was in plain sight. But soon, Brady knew that he must head back. His mom would be expecting him!

The sunshine felt so good on Brady and Tango, it seemed as if it were watching over them. It was a beautiful October day in Sitka. Brady and Tango were both so glad to be out and about enjoying the outdoors. However, when they finally arrived back at the beach where they left the kayak, it was gone! (2) Brady could not believe it. He was in big trouble. He must not have tied up his kayak with a good enough knot, and when the tide and waves came in, it was washed away. Brady could not see his kayak, and even though he could see the airport, he knew he could not cross it. Brady was not sure what to do. He was no longer noticing the sunshine...he was worried!

He headed back towards a little campsite he had noticed while walking and decided to start a fire to keep warm. (7) Since the woods in Sitka are almost always wet from the rain, Brady always carried fire starter and various other survival items in his fanny pack. Brady had to search underneath the large trees for small dry twigs to start his fire with.

Tango seemed to understand that Brady was worried and stayed extra close to comfort him. Brady was so glad that Tango was there for company! However, Brady could not rest for long, he needed more firewood.

As Brady was looking for firewood, he became sidetracked and started collecting rounded beach rocks to build little rock people. As he finished and was admiring his work, Tango walked by and knocked over the rocks with his tail. That silly dog! Just as Brady was thinking that nothing was going right, he caught sight of something floating in the water.

Brady squinted into the bright, setting sunshine and saw the most amazing sight — his kayak! It had floated with the current all the way around a large peninsula and was floating near him just off of the beach. (8) Brady could not believe his luck! But how could he get to his kayak? The ocean water was only around 50 degrees, and Brady knew it would be very dangerous to get wet. He could get so cold that hypothermia would set in.

Tango watched Brady as Brady talked to him about his concerns. Then Brady got a great idea! It was a long shot, but Brady wondered if Tango might swim out to retrieve his kayak! Brady had played fetch with Tango many times with sticks, frisbees, and balls. But, would Tango retrieve a kayak? Brady talked excitedly to Tango, and soon Tango was jumping around like a crazy dog!

Then, Brady pointed toward the kayak, and yelled, "Go fetch, Tango!" Tango took off like a shot! He swam all the way out to the kayak, found the tie-up line, and pulled the kayak back to shore! Brady could not believe it. Tango had saved the day!

When Tango got back to the beach, he was very tired. He lay down on the rocks for a while with the kayak rope by his face. Brady was so proud of Tango! Soon he put out their fire and kayaked back toward John Brown's Beach, where Brady's mom was waiting to take them home. Brady and Tango were exhausted and so happy to be home! Brady knew that Tango was a wonderful friend and the bravest dog ever!

The End

Brady '14

This is a picture of Tango at 8 weeks old. Sitka Tango is now an 18-month-old Nova Scotia Duck Tolling Retriever. He is a busy little dog and hopes to write about more adventures soon! Check out Sitka Tango's very own website at www.sitkatango.com.

About the Authors

Born and raised in Sitka, Alaska, authors Tracie and Brady Harang figured out a way to show others some of the excitement that can be found while living on an island in Southeast Alaska. Sitka has so much history to share, and the beauty of its rainforest is so amazing. Tracie and Brady incorporated both into a short adventure story. Although Sitka can have long stretches of damp, grey days, Tracie and Brady realize that this is why Sitka is so breathtakingly beautiful when the sun shines. The Harang family and their two dogs spend many weekends exploring the Southeast Alaska coast on their boat, the Sea Grace.